CW00522344

African Violets

In Search of the Wild Violets

by

Reinhild Raistrick

A monograph on the genus *Saintpaulia*

Dedicated to my mother
Hildegard Waltenberg neé Bokermann

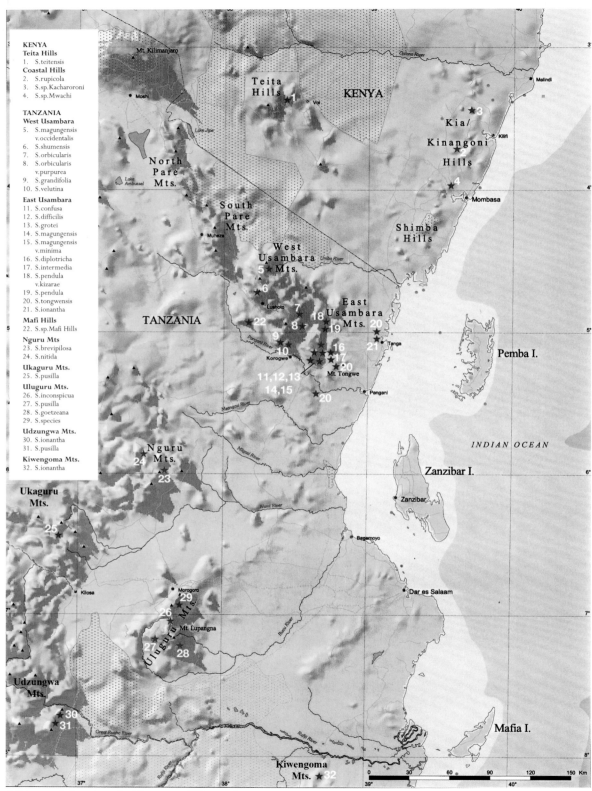

KENYA
Teita Hills
1. S.teitensis
Coastal Hills
2. S.rupicola
3. S.sp.Kacharoroni
4. S.sp.Mwachi

TANZANIA
West Usambara
5. S.magungensis
    v.occidentalis
6. S.shumensis
7. S.orbicularis
8. S.orbicularis
    v.purpurea
9. S.grandifolia
10. S.velutina
East Usambara
11. S.confusa
12. S.difficilis
13. S.grotei
14. S.magungensis
15. S.magungensis
    v.minima
16. S.diplotricha
17. S.intermedia
18. S.pendula
    v.kizarae
19. S.pendula
20. S.tongwensis
21. S.ionantha
Mafi Hills
22. S.sp.Mafi Hills
Nguru Mts
23. S.brevipilosa
24. S.nitida
Ukaguru Mts.
25. S.pusilla
Uluguru Mts.
26. S.inconspicua
27. S.pusilla
28. S.goetzeana
29. S.species
Udzungwa Mts.
30. S.ionantha
31. S.pusilla
Kiwengoma Mts.
32. S.ionantha

African violet sites in Kenya and Tanzania.

CONTENTS

Foreword

Every time I enter my house I am reminded of Mazumbai and the two memorable visits I made to the Usambara Mountains of Tanzania as a young botanist in the 1970s, shortly after I joined the staff of the Royal Botanic Gardens, Kew. The memories are sparked by Reinhild Raistrick's beautiful and detailed watercolour painting of *Streptocarpus caulescens* that hangs in my hallway. I cut my teeth as an African botanist on Mazumbai's plants. This wonderful forest survives in the West Usambaras to the present day through the far-sightedness of a Swiss couple, John and Lucy Tanner, who owned a large estate growing quinine (*Cinchona*). In the early 1980s, 2000 hectares of their forest was set aside by them as a nature reserve and given to the University of Dar-es-Salaam, along with their house as a research centre. Like Reinhild, John Tanner's family moved to Tanzania (then Tanganyika) in the last years of the 19th century. His father ran the Amboni estate on the coast near Tanga, and it was nearby that *Saintpaulia ionantha* and *Impatiens walleriana* were first collected and introduced into cultivation over a century ago.

I first met Reinhild almost 20 years ago when she brought some of her watercolour paintings to Kew for identification. I was enthralled by her easy style that captures the essence of the plants so well and cajoled her into selling me the *Streptocarpus* painting that I coveted. It has given me endless pleasure ever since and I have followed her progress as a botanical artist through her exhibitions and published illustrations in prestigious journals, such as Curtis's Botanical Magazine.

African violets are iconic, one of the most important of all plants in the nursery trade for pot-plants. Every year millions are sold in nurseries, super-markets and flower shops around the world. However, little, if any thought, is ever given to their exotic origin or to the current perilous state of the species and their shrinking habitats in East Africa. Because it is so well-known to the general public, the African violet has become an important flag-ship for plant conservation in East Africa. The relictual nature of its distribution, found now only in a few pockets in the Eastern Arc mountains of Tanzania and south-east Kenya, means that the species have always been rare, some so rare that their distribution is restricted to an area no larger than Kew Gardens. The relentless pressure on the local forests for timber, cultivation, mining and housing, means that all its habitats are now severely threatened. Indeed, populations in the more accessible sites have already disappeared as the forests have been cleared. Added to that has been the continuing collection of wild plants for horticulture that has decimated or even exterminated populations. African violets are truly a threatened group of plants but they also reflect the pressures on other native plants and animals whose habitats are annually diminishing through the activities of a growing and increasingly desperate human population.

Reinhild's beautiful watercolour illustrations show clearly what might be lost if habitats are not protected in the region. Some sites do indeed have protected status, but without local awareness and realisation of the value of forest for providing clean water and sustainable resources for the local people, many habitats will continue to disappear even in protected places.

I have now reached an age where I am aware of how much has disappeared from the places I knew as a boy in England. During nearly 40 years working as a botanist in the tropics, I have also seen forests clear-felled on an alarming scale throughout the tropics. The realisation that the world's climate depends upon the maintenance of tropical forests is slowly changing political imperatives throughout the world. I hope that action to save what remains is rapid enough to save the few pristine areas that remain in the Eastern Arc mountains. This fine memoir will surely raise awareness and concern both here and in East Africa. We can all make a difference where conservation is concerned. In this fine book of a disappearing icon, Reinhild has set an excellent example and one that hopefully will make a difference.

Phillip Cribb
The Royal Botanic Gardens,
Kew
June 2006

The Usambara Forests shrouded in mist.

CHAPTER ONE

Background to the search for the wild violet

In the mid 1990s I went to the Usambara Mountains in Tanzania for an extended period, in order to paint flowers of the region. As I went to the remote areas, often trekking long distances on foot, with African guides, they called me 'a child of the forest'. We conversed with each other in Kiswahili and Kishambaa (the local tribal language) about fruits, nuts, trees and streams, which I recollected from childhood, and we shared common experiences. I had returned to the remote forest region where I was born in 1940. Not only was this my birthplace, but that of my mother in 1907. This was also the area where my grandfather, Wilhelm Bokermann, first came and settled in 1895. I had returned to my 'roots in the forest.' Where was this forest and what led to three generations of a family living in this place? It all had to do with a complex matrix of factors – geographical, historical, climatical, as well as social issues such as slavery, colonialism, and religious persuasions.

Forest location

The East and West Usambara Mountains together with the Mlinga-Magrotto ridge are situated in North East Tanzania, and form part of the Eastern Arc Mountains. They are separated into three blocks by deep valleys which run from north to south. The most important of these is the Lwengera Valley, which divides the East and West Usambaras; the Mlinga-Magrotto ridge is further separated from East Usambara by the Sigi Valley. The mountains range from 900m upwards, with the highest peaks in West Usambara reaching an altitude of 2300m; whereas in the eastern mountains they peak at 1506m at Nilo, in the Lutindi block. The East Usambaras tend to be less precipitous than the West, but the mountains rise steeply from the plains on all sides. These steep scarps and the deeply dissected nature of the uplands have an important effect on the climate of the region. Daytime temperature is largely within the 15°C-30°C range, but drops somewhat lower at the highest altitude and rises towards the coast. Rainfall varies from less than 25cm near the plains to over 200cm in other parts. Most places receive between 100cm and 130cm of rainfall per year in two, or in some places three, rainy seasons. The mountains as a whole were under rainforest in early times; de-forestation has rapidly increased in the last 50 years with the expansion of the population. The Government Forest Reserves now form the bulk of remaining forested land. The soils of most of the mountain region are red to brown sandy loams, broken by many outcrops of gneiss. There are still some thick rich soils in some of the stream valleys, but most of the country is hillside, where soil is thin and quickly exhausted, or eroded away by continual cropping without rotation or fallowing. In the last twenty years projects have been initiated to involve the local communities in active land conservation, and it is hoped to reverse the trend in declining land quality, forest cover, bio diversity and water levels.

Recent history and our family involvement

As a young child I grew up in a remote part of the West Usambara Mountains, away from the main centres of population. The vast majority of the local people were Wasambaa (people of the country termed Usambara). The language they spoke was Kishambala, a Bantu-based language, although an increasing number spoke Kiswahili, the lingua franca of East Africa. The Shambala were primarily arable cultivators, relying on the hoe (jembe) as the main agricultural tool, but they also kept cattle and small stock. The main crops grown in the area were maize, beans, cassava, sweet potatoes, banana and sugar cane, with 'cash crops' of wattle bark, vegetables and coffee being produced for market sale. The people ate predominantly starchy foods. Although some of these practices remain, there have been considerable changes in the last 60 years, both in produce grown and customs. Population expansion has increased the demand for land; improved standards of living for many have changed eating habits; developing communications have meant more cash crops are produced for sale in the markets of Dar-es-Salaam and Tanga.

The Shambala have a rich historical tradition. An advanced kingdom state had been established three generations before Krapf, a German explorer and missionary, met with Kimweri, king of the Usambaras on July 24th 1848. Kimweri's kingdom stretched for 225km westward from the coast and 100km north to south, an area which Krapf estimated contained half a million people. Kimweri had considerable contact with the Arabs based at the coast and in Zanzibar. The trade route (and slave route) which passed through his territory at Pangani was important to the Arabs. They even erected a fort within Kimweri's domain at Mt. Tongwe, to keep open the trade route when Kimweri might have local trouble. The slave trade still persisted long after its formal abolition in the 'Old World'. Burton and Speke visited Tongwe Garrison in 1857. It remained manned by Baluchi soldiers until the Sultan of Zanzibar ceded to Germany his sovereign rights over this coastal sector in 1885. This was brought about following a show of force by five German warships dropping anchor off Zanzibar in August, 1885. In 1886 the German and British Governments agreed Colonial boundary divisions of East Africa.

Large tropical tree ferns in among the lush forest undergrowth.

Saintpaulia confusa was also collected by Baron Walter von St Paul-Illaire in the East Usambaras. It was not recognized as a different species until early plant breeders discovered that the two had different types of seed capsules, one of which was short and rounded and the other longer in form. This was very confusing, as it had been assumed that there was only the one species. Hence the specie name *confusa*. So began the explosive development of the humble African violet, which finally led to its being possibly the world's most popular house plant.

When preparing for my visit to the Usambaras, I came across another interesting family connection, that of my late father with the Illaire family. In the 1940s, when my father was confined by the British to Lutindi, as a Pastor in the Lutheran Church, he had prepared and confirmed two German children who at that time lived in Nairobi. They were the grandchildren of Baron Walter von St Paul-Illaire, who in the 1890s visited the Usambaras at the time when my grandfather was living in Lutindi. As I commenced my searches in the forest, I often wondered whether my grandfather and the Baron had had occasion to meet on their travels and mused that I was travelling the same pathways one hundred years later.

Searching the Forests

The East African specialists of the Royal Botanic Gardens, Kew, were very helpful in their advice and support of the work I was to undertake. They, together with Bill Burtt from the Royal Botanic Garden of Edinburgh, provided me with details of known sites where the African violet existed, mainly in the East Usambaras as well as the coastal forests. My mother, from her detailed knowledge of plant locations in the West Usambaras (particularly in the Mlalo/Lushoto region), suggested other possible places to reconnoitre.

Many expeditions led us into the more remote areas of this region. Some of the plant sites no longer exist, as forests have been cut down, exposing the delicate plants to strong sunlight. However, where forest reserves have been created, the plant colonies remain healthy. Because of my previous knowledge of the forest, we were able to identify some more sites to be added to the list. Possibly the happiest find was discovering a very healthy colony of *Saintpaulia grandifolia* growing in the forest at Lutindi, near where I had grown up as a child.

Entering the rainforest looking for flowers always filled me with an overwhelming

Enormous trees provide shade for plants below.

emotion evoking childhood memories, but also there was an excited anticipation of what I might find. The senses were triggered by the smell of the lush undergrowth, the sound of the birds, the movement in the trees overhead caused by the colobus monkeys, accompanied by their distinctive 'Nje, Nje, Nje,' call, or the rising steam following a downpour of rain. I was usually accompanied by at least two foresters, who carried with them a panga (machete) used to cut away the dense undergrowth that overhung the narrow pathways, and also as a weapon to confront the occasional wild pig.

We entered the forest, which was darkened by the rich canopy of indigenous trees, often festooned with trailing lianas. The occasional pathways we criss-crossed were routes taken by people from one village to another, situated on the outer edges of the forest. As we traversed fast-flowing mountain streams with shaded banks, I would scan the slopes for the siting of an African violet or even a *Streptocarpus*. Both herbaceous plants need shade, dampness and warmth for ideal growing conditions. Once we heard the rasping sound of a saw in the distance and disturbed an illegal pit sawing activity in progress. A large camphor tree had been cut down, creating a gap in the tree canopy. This illegal logging, if left unchecked, could change the delicate balance of the forest, by opening up the canopy and allowing direct sunlight through to the forest floor, and thus destroying some of the existing plant life which is dependent on shade.

We would often traverse three distinct climatic zones as we trekked long distances through the forest; firstly the lush thick undergrowth of the lower slopes with huge tree ferns in abundance, followed by the montane forests with lichen hanging from the tree branches, and finally on to the high altitude slopes with scrub and tree heathers.

As we walked through the forests, I would often point out certain plants or trees and describe what we used them for as children, for example, the small trees, from which we made wooden wheels for our 'go-carts', or the delicious, green-mottled fruit from the tall Mula tree, which the monkeys or bush babies also relished. As people passed we would greet them with the extended and complex greetings of the Shambala.

Follow up
Finding the African violet was sometimes the easy part of the expedition. No matter what the time of day and the possible difficulties with driving back to base in the dark, I wanted to make detailed sketches of the plant *in situ*, recording also the altitude and general position. If it was a healthy plant and there were a number of others in the

A forester from the Amani Reserve collecting a *Saintpaulia* specimen for Kew.

locality, I had been given permission to collect one specimen. We often had a long journey back to our home, through differing climatic zones, and so I carried the flower in an inflated plastic bag, adding a few drops of stream water to maintain its own 'eco system'. On returning home, tired and elated, after a long muddy or dusty drive, I would attempt a more detailed drawing and painting, before pressing the specimen. This was then taken to the Lushoto Herbarium for onward transmission to Kew. I pressed specimens of all plants and flowers that I painted, including orchids and impatients etc. in order to assist with identification at the Kew Herbarium on my return to Europe. I cannot speak too highly of all the support given by the staff at Lushoto Herbarium under the guidance of Mr Ruffo. His whole team showed great interest in my drawings and many a discussion ranged on the correct identification of plants, their usage and other sightings of the *Saintpaulia* genus. They were invaluable with their knowledge of their trees and forests.

Not all the trips were smooth and uneventful. Often we travelled long distances to find that the sites had either been destroyed by illegal tree-cutting, cattle-grazing or by cultivation. Sometimes the roads were impassable and on occasions we could not even find the site as described by previous collectors. We did not have the luxury of satellite navigation systems to assist us. Some of the incidents we encountered I have written as additional descriptions to the paintings.

It was an amazing period in my life when I was able to have the opportunity to do what I love, painting flowers growing in their natural habitat. The great joy in recording the beautiful flowers of the Usambaras such as the orchids, busy lizzies, begonias, and most especially the African violet, and returning home to my country of origin to be once again a 'child of the forest,' was beyond words.

Saintpaulia grotei

This plant was found growing on Mt Mlinga, East Usambara, in a small area of forest surrounding the peak, where the steepness of the slopes prevented any cultivation. The plant had a trailing habit with one or two violet flowers on each peduncle. The leaves were thin and round with long and short appressed hairs. This was a more delicate plant than *S. magungensis* which was found nearby. We trekked up this coastal mountain with foresters, on a very hot day, and half way up I was overcome with heat exhaustion and had to withdraw into the shade. The foresters duly brought back the two different plants for me to illustrate. I had my painting equipment with me and after my recovery and the disappointment of not being able to climb to the top, I settled down to paint the beautiful water lily, *Nymphea nouchali,* seen growing in a nearby pond. This painting appears in Chapter 5.

Painted on site in November 1991.

Later identified as *Saintpaulia grotei* A. Engler.

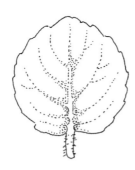

Leaf × 1

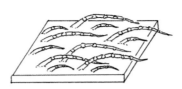

Long and short
appressed leaf hairs × 15

Immature fruit
capsule × 3

Saintpaulia magungensis **var.** *occidentalis*

We trekked a long way through the West Usambara, from Mlalo to Bagai, to get to this beautiful forest area on the edge of the escarpment overlooking the plains, at an altitude of 1200m. The banks on either side of the path were covered in these trailing plants. As the short rains had been, the plants already laden with flower buds would be a mass of dark-blue blooms within a few weeks. The dark, slightly glossy leaves with medium and short appressed hairs, had a reddish underside, as had the hairy peduncles and thick stems. There was a village nearby and felling of trees much in evidence. How long would this special site remain?

Painted on site in December 1991.

Later identified as *Saintpaulia magungensis* E. Roberts var. *occidentalis* B. L. Burtt.

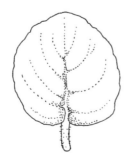

Leaf × ³/4

Medium and short
appressed leaf hairs × 20

Fruit capsule × 3

Saintpaulia orbicularis

Of all the *saintpaulias* painted in the wild this was possibly the most delicate. It was in a very vulnerable position in the remaining forest. It was found near Ambangulu, West Usambara, at the edge of a tea plantation at an altitude of 1200m. This small colony was on a bank above a track and a lot of soil had recently been excavated for brick making. The future for these plants certainly did not seem secure. The very pale-lilac flowers, with deep mauve centres, were held up on long thin peduncles, giving this plant a look of fragility. The thin leaves were heart-shaped and mid-green in colour with pale undersides and reddish veining leading off from the rather long red petioles. The upper surface was covered in short appressed hairs of variable length.

Painted on site in December 1991.

Later identified as *Saintpaulia orbicularis* B. L. Burtt.

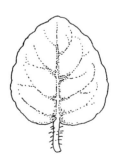

Leaf × 3/4

Short and medium
appressed leaf hairs × 10

Fruit capsule × 1 3/4

Saintpaulia tongwensis

I was informed by some botanists working for the Frontier-Tanzania Coastal Forest Research Programme, that possibly a new *Saintpaulia* species was to be found in the Genda-Genda Forest, inland from Pangani. After a long, hot trek we were rewarded not only with a refreshing swim in a stream nearby, but also by the sight of a healthy colony of these plants. Their large, hairy leaves were hanging somewhat due to the heat and dryness. The short rains had not yet been, but the coastal forest scrub gave sufficient protection from the hot sun above. The plants grew as a large single crown with short, reddish petioles, holding thick pale-green leaves. They were ovate and markedly pointed and covered in long erect hairs, again as with so many of the coastal species. The pale-blue flowers were held erect on thick pink peduncles.

Painted on site in January 1992.

Not a new species, as might have been hoped, but later identified as *Saintpaulia tongwensis* B. L. Burtt.

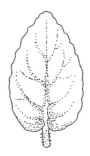

Leaf × ¹/₂

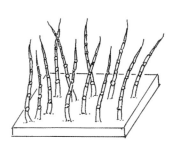

Long erect
leaf hairs × 10

Fruit capsule × 3

Saintpaulia grandifolia

Of all the *saintpaulias* painted in the wild, this was, without doubt, for me the most special. I found and illustrated this specimen in Lutindi, West Usambara, the place of my birth and where I grew up as a child, playing in these forests. This small area of forest still remains fairly untouched; however, land is at a premium and there is an expanding village nearby. The short rains had been, after a long dry spell, and the large leaves, as the name implies, were green and healthy with long erect hairs. The clusters of violet flowers brightened up the forest. It was a truly wonderful sight.

Painted on site in January 1992.

Later identified as *Saintpaulia grandifolia* B. L. Burtt.

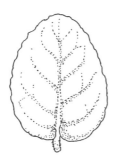

Leaf × ¹/₂

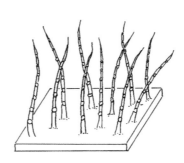

Dense long erect
leaf hairs × 15

Fruit capsule × 2

46

CHAPTER FOUR

African violets in British and European Collections

In 2000, I met another enthusiast of the wild African violet, the plant genus *Saintpaulia*. He was also born in Tanzania and spent much of his early years in the Tanga region. Colin Watkins was aware of the conservation status of this endangered genus and with great enthusiasm set off to track down all the species held *ex-situ* in botanic gardens throughout Britain and Europe. He visited gardens in Uppsala, Helsinki, Meise (Brussels), Kew and Edinburgh amongst others. Colin was able to procure from these gardens many of the species I had not painted in the wild and I am most grateful to him and the garden authorities for providing me with the precious plants.

He also travelled to Tanzania to seek those species that were not held in any botanic garden anywhere in the world. He received official permits from the Tanzania Government to collect herbarium material for the National Herbarium of Tanzania and living material for the Royal Botanic Garden, Edinburgh. This garden specialises in the plant family Gesneriaceae, which includes *Saintpaulia*. Some of the material he collected and sent to the Royal Botanic Garden, Edinburgh, was grown on by them and sent to me to paint and record.

No *ex-situ* holding in any botanic garden has a complete collection of *Saintpaulia* and I believe that it would be a good thing to be able to see them all under one roof in Tanzania or in Europe. Nevertheless, I have been able to put together a unique record by painting all the species of wild African violets held in various botanic gardens. A complete set is now possible, as the missing *Saintpaulia* species were collected by the Edinburgh-based Dr Elspeth Haston, a taxonomist specialising in Gesneriaceae, during two expeditions to the Uluguru Mountains, Tanzania, in 2005. Amongst other plants, she re-discovered and collected the very rare (it had been thought to be extinct) *Saintpaulia inconspicua,* the equally rare *Saintpaulia goetzeana* and *Saintpaulia pusilla.* Some living material from these species, together with a possible new species, Dr Haston collected, are now being grown on in the Royal Botanic Garden, Edinburgh. It has been a delight to paint these special plants, unseen or unrecognised, for almost a century.

Revision of the taxonomy of the genus *Saintpaulia* is being undertaken by Dr Iain Darbyshire, a taxonomist at the Herbarium in Kew. This revised taxonomy is to be formally published in the near future as part of *Flora Tropical East Africa FTEA*. I have therefore continued to use the species descriptions by B. L. Burtt that have been in use for several decades.

Saintpaulia goetzeana.

Saintpaulia diplotricha

Distribution   East Usambara Mountains, Tanzania

This plant was painted from a collection at the University of Cambridge Botanic Garden. It was a lush plant with many peduncles, all holding 4-7 pale lilac blooms. The leaves were thick, heart-shaped, dark green with marked pale veining, some turning upwards. The leaves were also somewhat quilted in texture, with pale red undersides, and the petioles and peduncles a pale pink. The upper surfaces of the leaves were covered in long and short erect hairs.

Species description by B. L. Burtt in 1958.

Painted in October 2002.

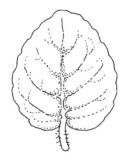

Leaf × ³/₄

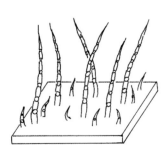

Long and short erect
leaf hairs × 13

Fruit capsule × 2 ¹/₂

50

Saintpaulia magungensis **var.** *minima*

Distribution   East Usambara Mountains, Tanzania

This plant was painted from the collection at the University of Cambridge Botanic Garden, where they grow profusely, spreading across the floor of the tropical glasshouse in a truly trailing manner. This specimen, potted up from the collection, was particularly healthy, with many fairly large-sized purple flowers, 1-2 per peduncle. The leaves were probably larger than the small wild ones would be, as their name implies, and were covered in long and short appressed hairs.

Species description by B. L. Burtt in 1964.

Painted in June 2003.

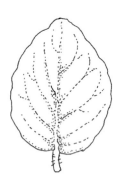

Leaf × 1

Long and short appressed
leaf hairs × 20

Fruit capsule × 3

Saintpaulia pendula

Distribution   East Usambara Mountains, Tanzania

This wonderful specimen, with its abundance of pale to medium blue-violet flowers came from the species collection at 'The African Violet World', King's Lynn. It has more than one flower per peduncle, therefore rather more resembling *S pendula* var. *kizarae*. A good trailing plant, as its name implies, with mid-green rounded leaves. The red colouring extends from the petiole into the veining on the pale green underside of the leaf. The leaves are covered with short, erect hairs.

Species description by B. L. Burtt in 1958.

Painted in August 2002.

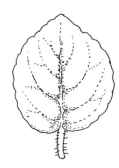

Leaf × 1

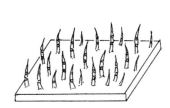

Dense and short erect
leaf hairs × 6

Fruit capsule × 4

Saintpaulia pendula **var.** *kizarae*

Distribution   East Usambara Mountains, Tanzania

This plant was from the Royal Botanic Garden of Edinburgh collection. There are 2 to 4 mid-blue violet flowers per peduncle. The leaves are ovate with an olive-green colouring above and pale green below. It has a trailing habit with fairly long reddish petioles. The leaves are covered with short, erect hairs.

Species description by B. L. Burtt in 1964.

Painted in June 2003.

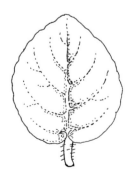

Leaf × 1

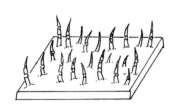

Short erect
leaf hairs × 7

Fruit capsule
– not seen

Saintpaulia intermedia

Distribution   East Usambara Mountains, Tanzania

This plant was obtained from a species collection at the 'African Violet World', King's Lynn. Further material to complete the painting was obtained from the National Botanic Garden, Meise. The rosette form also shows this mature specimen to have a trailing habit. The medium-sized leaves are dark-green with a slight red tinge above, gained from the deep-red colouring below. They are covered in dense suberect white hairs, giving the whole plant a soft, velvet look. Each pink peduncle holds 4-6 blue-violet flowers.

As with most of the species when grown in an *ex-situ*, warm glasshouse environment, they do particularly well and flower profusely.

Species description by B. L. Burtt in 1958.

Painting completed in February 2006.

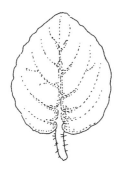

Leaf × 1

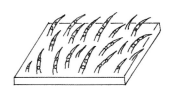

Dense suberect short
leaf hairs × 8

Fruit capsule × 4

Saintpaulia tongwensis

Distribution   East Usambara Mountains and Coastal Plain Forests, Tanzania

This plant was obtained from the species collection at the 'African Violet World', King's Lynn. It is different from the species found in the wild; the leaves are ovate, but less pointed. There is pronounced, pale-green veining on the slightly darker leaves; the petioles are also longer, with a more open crown. The pale-blue flowers are similar to their wild counterpart, but much more prolific, as the plants had been grown in a glass house. The leaves are also covered in long erect hairs.

Iain Darbyshire says this unusual form is probably from Sigi Falls, East Usambara.

Species description by B. L. Burtt in 1947.

Painted in August 2002.

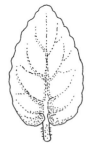

Leaf × ¹/₂

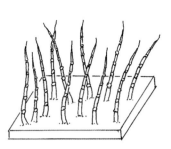

Long erect
leaf hairs × 10

Fruit capsule × 3

Saintpaulia orbicularis **var.** *purpurea*

Distribution   West Usambara Mountains, Tanzania

This plant was painted from the collection of the Royal Botanic Garden of Edinburgh. The flowers, borne 6 to 9 blooms per stalk, are a much darker purple than those of the typical variety *orbicularis,* which was painted from the wild. The glossy leaves are also slightly darker and more pointed in shape, with short appressed hairs.

The fruit seen from Herbarium material for the drawing, was possibly immature, as one would expect to see it similar to the fruit var. *orbicularis*, as on page 42.

Species description by B. L. Burtt in 1964.

Painted in June 2003.

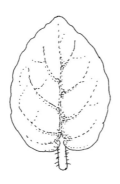

Leaf × ²/₃

Short appressed
leaf hairs × 13

Immature fruit
capsule × 3

Saintpaulia sp. from Mafi Hills

Distribution   Hills southwest of West Usambara Mountains, Tanzania

This plant, collected in the field by Colin Watkins and the Tanzanian National Herbarium, was sent back and grown on by the Royal Botanic Garden of Edinburgh in February 2003. It arrived safely on my doorstep in July 2004, with a mass of violet-blue flowers, 2-5 per peduncle. The dark green leaves were ovate, thick and shiny, with reddish undersides, and a tendency to fold over. The upper surface was sparsely covered with short appressed hairs.

It is to be published in the Flora Tropical East Africa as *Saintpaulia ionantha* subsp. *mafiensis* I. Darbysh. & Pócs.

Painted in July 2004.

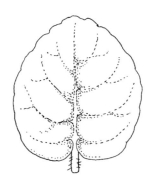

Leaf × 1

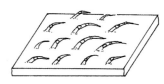

Sparse short appressed
leaf hairs × 13

Fruit capsule × 3

Saintpaulia shumensis

Distribution   West Usambara Mountains, Tanzania

I was not able to locate this species in the wild. It comes from the Shume forest in West Usambara, growing at an altitude of 1900m, where frosts can occur. This hardy plant is covered in a layer of long, erect hairs and has possibly one of the paler of the flowers in the *Saintpaulia* range. The pale-violet blooms have a darker centre and stand out against dark green shiny leaves.

This plant was obtained from the species collection at the 'African Violet World', King's Lynn.

Species description by B. L. Burtt in 1955.

Painted in June 2002.

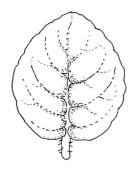

Leaf × 1

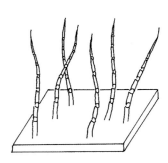

Long erect
leaf hairs × 10

Fruit capsule × 2

Saintpaulia velutina

Distribution   West Usambara Mountains, Tanzania

This plant was also obtained from the species collection at the 'African Violet World', King's Lynn. This species with its dark, velvety leaves is very distinctive. The deep red undersides have given the green leaves this dark colouring and the quilted surface is covered in long and short erect hairs. The flowers held up on red peduncles are a pale blue-violet, with a dark centre. A most attractive species.

Species description by B. L. Burtt in 1958.

Painted in June 2002.

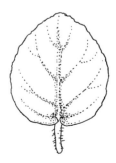

Leaf × 1

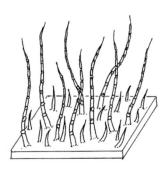

Long and short erect
leaf hairs × 12

Immature fruit
capsule × 1 ½

Saintpaulia brevipilosa

Distribution   Nguru Mountains, Tanzania

This healthy plant came from the National Botanic Garden, Meise. The rounded leaves had wide, pale green veining and were quite glossy, the surface being covered with short, erect hairs. The flowers were noticeably small and pale-purple with darker centres. These were carried on delicate, pink peduncles. The petioles were also pink, the colour being carried through onto the surface of the underside of the pale green leaves.

Species description by B. L. Burtt in 1964.

Painted in October 2002.

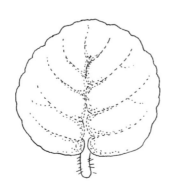

Leaf × 1

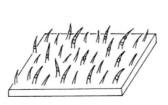

Dense very short erect
leaf hairs × 20

Fruit capsule × 2

Saintpauli nitida

Distribution   Nguru Mountains, Tanzania

This plant was painted from the collection of the National Botanic Garden, Meise. A healthy specimen grown in cultivation would therefore have slightly bigger blooms than those growing in the wild. The leaves were rounded and wax shiny, with reddish colouring below, giving a slight red hue to the mid-green colour above. They were covered with short appressed hairs.

Species description by B. L. Burtt in 1958.

Painted in October 2002.

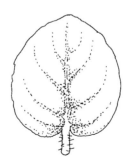

Leaf × ¹/₂

Dense short appressed
leaf hairs × 10

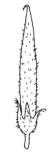

Immature fruit
capsule × 1 ¹/₂

Saintpaulia rupicola

Distribution   Kinangoni Hills, Kenya

This plant came from the University of Cambridge Botanic Garden. The light-blue flowers are held erect above the medium-green leaves with paler undersides. This particular specimen had quite an open crown, with fairly long reddish petioles. The leaves were covered with short, erect hairs.

Species description by B. L. Burtt in 1964.

Painted in October 2002.

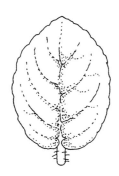

Leaf × ²/₃

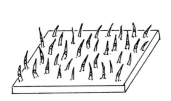

Short erect
leaf hairs × 5

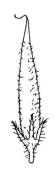

Fruit capsule × 1 ¹/₅

Saintpaulia teitensis

Distribution   Teita Hills, Kenya

This plant, from the National Botanic Garden, Meise, has particularly dark green, shiny leaves, with long erect hairs. The long petioles are reddish-purple, as are the reverse sides of the leaves. The fairly dark-blue flowers, on short peduncles, are clustered around the crown of this specimen.

Species description by B. L. Burtt in 1958.

Painted in April 2003.

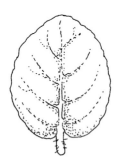

Leaf × ¹/₂

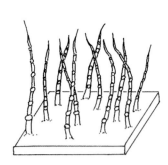

Long erect
leaf hairs × 25

Fruit capsule × 1 ¹/₄

Saintpaulia sp. **Kacharoroni**

Distribution   Kenya Coastal Hills

This healthy plant came from the collection at the National Botanic Garden, Meise. The crown of the specimen is shown growing from the original leaf. The thick, hairy leaves also show some variation with yellow markings. The upper surfaces are covered with suberect hairs. The flowers are a pale blue colour and grow 2-3 per peduncle.

This is considered by some to be a distinct undescribed species, but I. Darbyshire believes this to be a form of *Saintpaulia rupicola*.

Painted in April 2003.

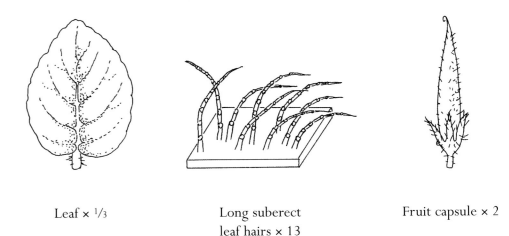

Leaf × 1/3

Long suberect
leaf hairs × 13

Fruit capsule × 2

Saintpaulia sp. **Mwachi**

Distribution   Kenya Coastal Hills

This robust plant was also obtained from the collection of the National Botanic Garden, Meise. The thick stem and crowded crown have a slightly trailing habit. The thick, ovate, pointed leaves have strong markings, giving them a marbled look. They are held on long red petioles. The upper surfaces of the leaves are covered with suberect hairs. The 6-8 pale blue flowers are held erect on pink peduncles. With its thick hairy leaves it has the appearance of a true coastal species.

I. Darbyshire believes this also to be a form of *Saintpaulia rupicola*.

Painted in April 2003.

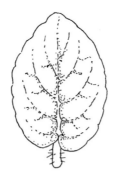

Leaf × $^2/_3$

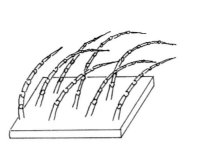

Long suberect
leaf hairs × 15

Fruit capsule × 2

Saintpaulia inconspicua

Distribution   Uluguru Mountains, Tanzania

This small plant with tiny pale, near-white blooms has a trailing tendency. The specimen I painted had quite a thick stem, with new groups of leaves growing off it. The leaves were pale green, hairless and noticeably shiny, so different from the typical hairy *Saintpaulia* leaf. However, the flowers had that typical African violet appearance. This small plant with its tiny flower, will be quite 'inconspicuous' in the deep shade of the high Uluguru cloud forest.

Painted in 2002 from a plant procured by Colin Watkins prior to its dispatch to the Royal Botanic Garden, Edinburgh.

Species description by B. L. Burtt in 1958.

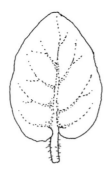

Leaf × 1

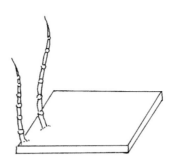

Sparse long erect hairs
on leaf margin × 20

Fruit capsule × 3

Saintpaulia pusilla

Distribution   Uluguru Mountains, Tanzania

This is one of the earliest known species. It was collected by W. Goetze in 1898, but is no longer held in any known collection. Dr E. Haston, from the Edinburgh Botanic Garden, visited the Uluguru Mountains in 2005, and collected herbarium material. This species is a miniature. The tiny white flowers have violet-blue upper lobes and a distinct corolla tube. The small, broadly ovate leaves have sparse, long erect hairs on the upper surface and are purple-tinged below. The plants grow at an altitude of 1200m to 1800m.

I was able to complete a painting of the *Saintpaulia pusilla* in May 2006, by using archival drawings by A. Engler and herbarium specimens.

Species description by A. Engler in 1900.

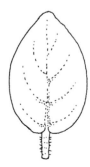

Leaf × 1 ¼

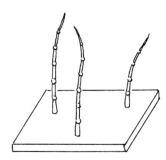

Sparse long erect
leaf hairs × 15

Fruit capsule × 4

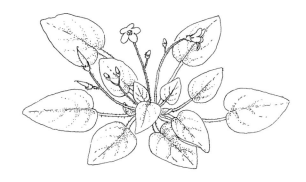

× ³/₄

Saintpaulia goetzeana

Distribution   Uluguru Mountains, Tanzania

This is possibly the most striking of all the *Saintpaulia* species. It was also one of the earliest known species. It was collected by W. Goetze in 1898.

Due to its particular growing conditions in the wild, it is very difficult to grow *ex situ* and bring into flower, and is therefore not seen in collections.

This was another important find by Dr E. Haston as few botanists have seen this species in flower. She describes the beautiful blooms as being bi-coloured, with the three lower petals white and the two upper petals violet-blue. The trailing plant has dark green hairy leaves, with pale veining and purplish undersides. The upper surface has a dense covering of long erect hairs.

At the time of painting in May 2006, this specimen at Edinburgh had not yet flowered. The flowers were painted by using photographs and herbarium specimens.

Species description by A. Engler in 1900.

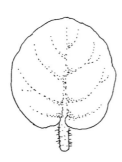

Leaf × 1

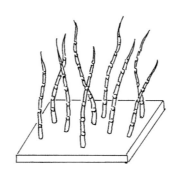

Dense long erect
leaf hairs × 20

Fruit capsule × 4

Saintpaulia **species**

This unidentified species of *Saintpaulia* was found by Dr E. Haston in the Uluguru Mountains in 2005. She described it as having large, pale leaves, with a similar appearance to *Saintpaulia rupicola*. However, the single rather wilted flower appeared to be very different. She also describes the leaves as glandular hairy. This is unique in Saintpaulia leading to further evidence that this might indeed be a new species. The living material is now being grown on in the Royal Botanic Garden, Edinburgh.

Identification of the possible new species will have to wait until it flowers.

At the time of painting in May, 2006, this specimen had not yet flowered. The flower and seed capsule were painted by using herbarium specimens and photographs taken on site by Dr Haston.

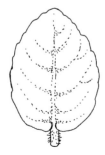

Leaf × ²/₃

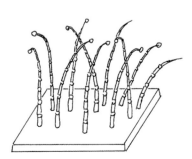

Dense long erect
glandular leaf hairs × 20

Immature fruit
capsule × 3

The beautiful mountain range of the West Usambaras.

These unique forests contain many indigenous trees and plants.

CHAPTER FIVE

Other flowers of the Usambara Rainforest

The forests of the Usambaras are unique in that they contain many indigenous trees and plants. However, although exotic, many of the flowers are very familiar, growing as household plants in our homes. There are many varieties of *Impatiens* in different hues of reds and pinks, gracing the forest floor where the light has managed to get through. Trailing *Begonia*, with clusters of pink and white blooms, make their way high into the trees. Tree orchids perch on the branches of tall trees, unseen to human eye, but drawing attention to any passing pollinator by their heady perfume. The banks of the fast-flowing streams are covered by many varieties of ferns and the great tree ferns *Cyatheaceae* block out the light. On overhanging rocks might be seen a small leaved *Streptocarpus*, with the elegant purple flowers on long, slender stalks, or even a small colony of *Saintpaulia*, sharing the same growing conditions; sharing the same family name of *Gesneriaceae*.

The trees are spectacular in size and shape. Huge buttresses block the path. Occasionally the ground will be covered in a confetti of white flowers, or strewn with nuts from the burst *Alanblackia* fruit pod.

The following paintings are just a selection of some of the treasures these forests contain.

Pressed specimens of all the plants painted were sent back to the Royal Botanic Gardens, Kew, via the Lushoto Herbarium. On my return to Kew, my paintings and pressed specimens were brought together to facilitate plant identification.

Gladiolus rupicolus

On my first visit to this amazing Mazumbai forest, which has been set aside as a reserve by the University of Dar-es-Salaam, I spent some time searching out the various unique flowers to be found here. On our second day, the foresters suggested we climb to the top of the mountain nearby, as they knew of some 'red' flowers growing there. We set off, first climbing the lower slopes, with lush, thick undergrowth and tree ferns lining the fast running streams to come to the next layer of montane forest. This was higher and a different forest zone, with lichen hanging from the trees, and less undergrowth below. We finally reached the top after a few hours' climb, arriving at a ridge above the forest at an altitude of 1900m. This open rocky area was covered with scrub and tree heathers. A shock met our eyes. The 'red' flowers had been dug up and they were strewn across the ridge. The culprits? They were the wild pigs, who feed voraciously on the corms of the stunning scarlet *Gladiolus rupicolus*. The wild pigs can become a problem in a reserve area, as no culling takes place, and therefore their numbers increase without control. (The balance between man and nature can so easily be disturbed). This erect herb with its bright red flowers is fairly common on other mountain peaks of the Usambaras. It usually grows in dry rocky places, preferring a more open aspect and is always such a rewarding sight at the end of a long hot climb.

A herbarium specimen was sent back to Royal Botanic Gardens, Kew, via the Lushoto Herbarium and was duly identified as the above.

Painted December 1990.

Impatiens mazumbaiensis

This species is named after Mazumbai, a tea estate in the West Usambara Mountains. Mr & Mrs Tanner, owners of the estate, generously gave a large piece of the wonderful, unspoilt, Mazumbai Forest to the University of Dar-es-Salaam, for ecological studies of its unique flora and fauna. It has duly become a reserve and is much visited by scientists from many countries. Mrs Lucie Tanner was able to contribute enormously to the knowledge of orchids in the forest around her, and she worked in close conjunction with Dr Phillip Cribb of the Royal Botanic Garden, Kew, in order to have these recorded.

I found this small, rather delicate plant growing by a stream in the Mazumbai Forest. It was supported by lush vegetation. Only the pale-pink flowers, with a magenta spot on the lateral petals, stood out among the verdant greens.

This species is endemic to the West Usambara Mountains. I was delighted to have found it and to have had the opportunity of painting a flower named after this amazing forest in which I had spent much time illustrating flowers.

A herbarium specimen was sent back to the Royal Botanic Gardens, Kew, and Dr Kit Grey-Wilson, who has written a definitive book on *Impatiens*, kindly identified this, together with the other *Impatiens* species painted from the Usambaras.

Painted on site in December 1991.

Impatiens pseudoviola

This small *Impatiens* grows to a height of 20cm-40cm. It grows in damp, shady places, in amongst ferns and mosses. I found this group of plants in the Shume Forest growing on a mossy bank above a stream, at an altitude of 1900m. The pale pinkish-violet flowers have a deep magenta line running down the lower petals from a white basal spot. The leaves are also fairly small, spiralling up the pink fleshy stem. There was quite a large colony of this species growing on this forest site.

A herbarium specimen was sent back to the Royal Botanic Gardens, Kew, via the Lushoto Herbarium and was duly identified as the above.

Painted on site in November 1990.

Impatiens walleriana

This *Impatiens* with its showy, crimson-red flowers often appears in an area where the habitat has been disturbed by a tree falling, therefore allowing more light to come through the tree canopy. The bright-green leaves are rather translucent and shiny, with a pale-green underside. The flower is flat, with a large upper petal and the lateral petals almost equal in size. The fruit on this specimen were well developed, one having already burst and curled back on itself. A childhood game was to hold the ripe fruit in one's fist and then squeeze and let the exploding capsules give a sensation of wriggly worms. This particular colony of plants was by the roadside, above the Amani rapids. This was a favourite picnic spot of ours, where we were sometimes closely observed by shy colobus monkeys with their handsome black and white pelts.

This species has been known to horticulturists and various forms have been selected for cultivation.

A herbarium specimen was sent back to the Royal Botanic Gardens, Kew, via the Lushoto Herbarium and was duly identified as the above.

Painted on site in November 1991.

Streptocarpus pallidiflorus

This trailing plant from the forest in Mazumbai was painted *in situ*. It grows in most forest areas of the Usambara in shady wet areas, especially along the sides of streams. The fleshy bulbous stems bear ovate-elliptic entirely petiole leaves, and the small purple flowers are held erect by thin peduncles with 4-7 blooms. The delicate flowers have striped markings, surrounding the white centre within the corolla. This is hairy on the outside, as are the calyx and flower stems. The capsule becomes twisted as it ripens. I found this growing among ferns and the *Impatiens mazumbaiensis*.

Hybridization between *S. pallidiflorus* and *S. caulescens* is believed to be not uncommon in the West Usambara mountains. This specimen is somewhat intermediate with *S. caulescens*. The corolla of the true *S. pallidiflorus* is more strongly ventricose in the upper half of the flower as in page 103. (I. Darbyshire)

A herbarium specimen was sent back to the Royal Botanic Gardens, Kew, via the Lushoto Herbarium and was duly identified as the above.

Painted on site in December 1991.

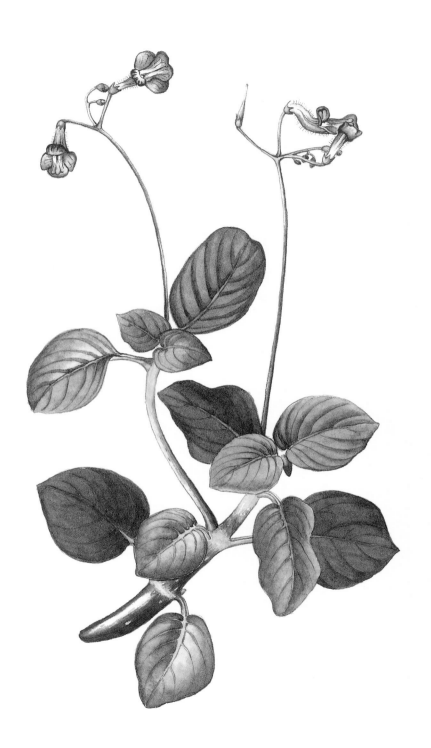

Eulophia streptopetala

This striking terrestrial orchid was found above the edge of the Mponde Forest, West Usambara, at an altitude of 1500m, in amongst scrub and rocks. The yellow flowers with green sepals have a sweet fragrance and a very distinctive 'lion's face'. The leaves, about 4cm wide, were well developed at the time of flowering. The ovoid pseudobulbs above the ground formed an interesting sculptural group. A fascinating orchid to paint.

A herbarium specimen was sent back to the Royal Botanic Gardens, Kew, via the Lushoto Herbarium and was duly identified as the above.

Painted on site in October 1990.

This painting is housed in the Library and Archives of the Royal Botanic Gardens, Kew.

Lobelia holstii

This elegant plant was found alongside a track, in a dry rocky place, at the edge of the Mponde Forest, West Usambara. The tall stem bears a few pale-mauve flowers. The small purple-tinged green leaves are lost in the undergrowth. Standing on its own, this is a most attractive plant.

A herbarium specimen was sent back to the Royal Botanic Gardens, Kew, via the Lushoto Herbarium and was duly identified as the above.

Painted on site in November 1990.

Aristea alata

This plant from the *Iridaceae* family was found growing in scrub, among tree heathers and the ground orchid, the *Brachycorythis pleistophylla*, above the forest line at an altitude of 1500m. The Mponde Forest in West Usambara remains fairly intact and the wild pig thrives within. While working on this *Aristea*, I could hear the pigs in the forest below and I felt safer to be above, as the wild pigs have a reputation for being very dangerous. They have been known to attack foresters and cause deep wounds.

 The bright blue flowers open only for a few hours and are then replaced by the next ones. This meant working fast in order to capture the fleeting blooms.

A herbarium specimen was sent back to the Royal Botanic Gardens, Kew, via the Lushoto Herbarium and was duly identified as the above.

Painted on site in January 1991.

Begonia meyeri-johannis

This trailing *Begonia* climbs high into the trees, bearing clusters of white-tinged pink flowers. It grows in the wet forest and this one was found in the Magamba Forest at an altitude of 1900m. The shiny dark leaves have bright-red veining above and below, with pale-green on the reverse side. The red stems also have distinctive markings, making this a most attractive woody forest climber.

A herbarium specimen was sent back to the Royal Botanic Gardens, Kew, via the Lushoto Herbarium and was duly identified as the above. However it was pointed out to me that I had shown only the male flowers and that, in fact, on this plant the flowers are unisexual. I therefore searched for another *Begonia* stem on my return visit the following year.

Painted on site in October 1990.

Begonia meyeri-johannis

The flowers on this woody forest climber are unisexual, with the male flower having two sepals, two petals, and many stamens, as can be seen in the top left cluster of the painting. The female flower has no stamens, but three stigmas, which are twisted and divided, and the ripening ovary can be seen in the painting at the bottom of the picture. The fruit capsules will produce many, minute seeds. This is a handsome plant with very attractive foliage.

A herbarium specimen was sent back to the Royal Botanic Gardens, Kew, via the Lushoto Herbarium and was duly identified as the above.

Painted on site in December, 1991.

Clerodendrum cephalanthum

This robust, woody climber was found in the Mponde Forest, West Usambara, at an altitude of 1600m. The heady perfume of the white blooms filled the air. The strongly veined leaves, with a rough texture, grow in whorls up the stem. The tubular flowers have a 5-lobed corolla and grow in clusters from the leaf junctions.

A herbarium specimen was sent back to the Royal Botanic Gardens, Kew, via the Lushoto Herbarium and was duly identified as the above.

Painted on site in November 1990.

This painting is housed in the Library and Archives of the Royal Botanic Gardens, Kew.

Gloriosa superba 'The Flame Lily'

This beautiful specimen was painted from a pot-grown plant. It had been grown from a V shaped tuber and produced these two striking, rather unusual, yellow blooms with brilliant red markings. As in the wild, the tips of the lanceolate leaves wound themselves around the supporting stakes in the pot.

These spectacular flowers grow at varying altitudes throughout East Africa. As a child, I was entranced by these showy blooms that were so conspicuous because of their brilliant colour – 'Flame Lily' - being a very apt name.

Painted in July 2004.

The natural habitat of the African violet is under increasing threat from deforestation.

Land is at a premium. The forest has had to make way for cultivation.

Conclusion

The 'African Violet' in various hybrid forms is one of the world's most popular house plants. They give immense pleasure and satisfaction to their owners. African Violet Societies exist throughout North America and Europe. This vast interest in the genus has developed from a somewhat insignificant flower originating in the Usambara Mountains, which form part of the Eastern Arc Mountains of Tanzania.

As a child, my love of wild flowers was stimulated by living alongside the rainforest and by my mother's deep knowledge and interest in the 'flowers of the forest'. It was she who introduced me to the wild African violets. It was through her interest in conserving the flowers in their natural habitat, that I was fired with the urge to continue in my search to record the complete known collection of this unique flower.

The Usambara Mountains are part of a designated biodiversity 'hot spot'. Unless conservation measures already introduced are sustained, then eventually the montane rainforests will gradually be reduced by man-made pressures and thus the natural habitat destroyed. Once the forest canopy is removed, light penetrates to the forest floor and plant life that requires shade and moisture disappears.

These Usambara forests, my childhood home, have provided the 'life blood' for the ultimate pleasure of thousands of African violet enthusiasts throughout the world. My hope is that this book will highlight:

The plight of the African violet in the wild

The need for individual involvement in the preservation and conservation of the Usambara Rainforest

The necessity for a botanical garden, both in East Africa and Europe or America, to bring together a complete collection of the wild African violet.

Acknowledgements

I wish to thank

Dr Phillip Cribb for his support and advice throughout.

Colin Watkins for his invaluable help in researching the African violet, and highlighting the conservation status of this genus.

Mr Ruffo and all the staff at the Lushoto Herbarium.

The Foresters from the Amani and Mazumbai Reserves.

The East African specialists at the Royal Botanic Gardens, Kew.

All the *ex-situ* collection holders and Botanic Gardens.

Mr Bill Burtt for his expertise in the Gesneriaceae family.

Dr Iain Darbyshire for his revised taxonomy on the genus *Saintpaulia*.

Dr Elspeth Haston, for enabling me to complete the painted collection.

Corinna Ravillious, Stephen Grady and Colin Watkins, for use of the map on Page 2.

Sieghard Waltenberg, Bokermann's great grandson, for his photographs of the Usambara Mountains, Tanzania.

Gebhard and Carolyn Waltenberg in Tanga, for their generous hospitality.

My grandchildren, who have loaned this fragile and beautiful earth to us for safe-keeping.

And finally, it is to Brian, my husband, companion and 'minder' that my thankfulness extends beyond measure. Without his love, support and enormous contribution, this book would not have happened.

Published in 2006 by Reinhild Raistrick
© Reinhild Raistrick SBA
ISBN 0-9554220-0-0
     978-0-9554220-0-3
A catalogue record for this book is available from the British Library

Printed by Healeys Printers 01473 461122
Origination by Dean Hearn